STANDING
O N   T H E
SIDELINES

By the same author:

Four O'Clock Friday

STANDING
ON THE
SIDELINES

Original poems by John Foster

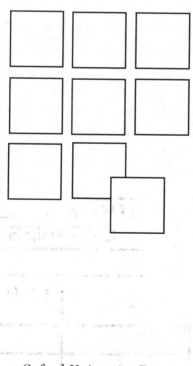

Oxford University Press
Oxford New York Toronto

Oxford University Press, Walton Street, Oxford OX2 6DP
Oxford New York Toronto
Delhi Bombay Calcutta Madras Karachi
Kuala Lumpur Singapore Hong Kong Tokyo
Nairobi Dar es Salaam Cape Town
Melbourne Auckland Madrid

and associated companies in
Berlin Ibadan

Oxford is a trade mark of Oxford University Press

Illustrated by Debbie Cook

ISBN O 19 276135 8 (hardback)
ISBN O 19 276136 6 (paperback)

A CIP catalogue record for this book is available from the
British Library

Printed in Hong Kong

Contents

Tall story   7

Life's a spelling test   8

Doctors   9

The day I became a vegetarian   10

Sarah, my sister, has asthma   11

Wait for me   12

Sisterly feelings   13

Just because you're my sister   14

Talking to the wall   15

'What makes you angry, Mum?'   15

Everything's fine   16

It's a dog's life   18

Mrs Nugent's budgie   19

The price   20

Guided tour   21

The perfect animal   22

Pistol practice   24

Facts about air   25

Summer storm   26

What is water?   27

Spells   28

What is a shooting star?   29

Moons   29

November   30

Winter   31

It's spring   32

In the still dark   33

Arctic skua   34

Christmas 1992   35
TV Wars (1991 version)   36
'It isn't right to fight'   37
Who's to say?   38
One of the many   39
Olympic circles   40
I dream of a time   41
Sing a song of censorship   42
Beware the Smile-a-Lot   42
Taking sides   43
Standing on the sidelines   44
Scene switching   45
The sporting spirit   46
Not the answer   47
And how was school today?   48
I dreamed a dolphin   49
Jane   50
Dad   51
Every other Sunday   52
Great-Grandad   53
Great-Aunt Charlotte   54
Farewell visit   55
Beneath the bridge   56
Then and Now   57
Where is the forest?   58
The Recycling Rap   59
Walls   61
Only one race   62
What is time?   63
Superstition   64

Tall story

Today, our teacher
Asked us to write
Lacrosse sticks in our English
Lesson. At least, that's what we thought

She said.
That's why most
Of us looked blank and
Replied, 'If it's all right with
You, we'd rather write high queues instead.'

Life's a spelling test

Life's a spelling test
When I ask you, 'What's your name?'
For I may spell it differently,
Although it sounds the same.

Are you Catherine with a C,
Or Katherine with a K,
Or Kathryn with a y,
Or Catharine with an a?

Is it Stephen with ph
Or Steven with a v?
Are you Glenn with double n?
Do I spell Ann(e) with an e?

Are you Sophie with ie
Or Sophy with a y?
Are you Jon without an h
Or Clare without an i?

Life's a spelling test,
It's your parents who're to blame.
What's on your birth certificate
Is how they spelt your name.

Doctors

Dr Aft is rough and ready.
Dr Unk's a bit unsteady.

Dr Omedary's got the hump.
Dr Ift's a snowy bump.

Dr Aught's a shivery chap.
Dr Owsy likes to nap.

Dr Um beats out a roll.
Dr Iver's in control.

Dr Agon's a fiery fighter.
Dr Acula's a late-night biter!

9

The day I became a vegetarian

When I was seven and a half,
I decided to become a vegetarian.

When I arrived home from school,
I told my mum.
'That's fine,' she said.
'It's up to you what you eat.
We're having meat.
The vegetables are over there.'

An hour later,
When Dad came home,
I sat down to eat
Like the rest of the family.
I'd decided to give up
Being a vegetarian.

Sarah, my sister, has asthma

Sarah, my sister, has asthma.
Sometimes, I wake up in the night
And hear her wheezing
In the bunk below.

I remember the time
I woke to hear her gasping for breath
And Mum had to call an ambulance.
They took her to the hospital
And kept her in for tests.

'She's allergic,' the doctor said.
'I expect she'll grow out of it.
Most young children do.'

Now she carries an inhaler
Everywhere she goes.

She gets annoyed when people
Try to stop her doing things.
She's always telling Grandma
To stop fussing.

'I'm not different,' she says.
'It's only asthma.
Lots of people have it.'

On Sports Day
Sarah came first in the high jump.
'You see, I'm not different,' she said.

Sarah, my sister, has asthma.
Sometimes I wake up in the night
And hear her wheezing
In the bunk below.

Wait for me

My brother Tim
Is three years older than me.

When I was six,
I could never keep up with him.
I remember
Running down the path after him
Shouting, 'Wait for me!
Wait for me!'

Since the accident,
Tim can't run any more.
Now, he sits in his chair,
Waiting for me
As I hurry on ahead
To open the gate
And help him down the steps.

Sisterly feelings

When my sister Gemma
was very, very ill,
I felt bad
because of all the attention
and all the presents she had.
Then, Gemma died
and all I felt
was very, very sad.

Just because you're my sister

Just because you're my sister,
Why should I do what you do?
Just because you're my sister,
Why should I behave like you?

Everyone goes on and on
About how well you've done,
About the exams you've passed
And all the trophies you've won.

Why can't they leave me alone?
Why can't everyone see
I don't want to be a copy of you,
I just want to be valued as me.

Talking to the wall

My sister sits in her own world
With her Walkman blaring away
And when we try to talk to her
She doesn't hear a word we say.

But when she wants to talk to us
She pulls her earphones out
And if we do not answer her
She stamps her foot and shouts.

'What makes you angry, Mum?'

'What makes you angry, Mum?' I asked.

'When people lie and cheat and steal.
But most of all people
who couldn't care less
how other people feel.'

Everything's fine

First, we missed the turning off the motorway.
Don't ask me how!
I'd fallen asleep in the back.
I was woken by the shouting
As they tried to blame each other.
We had to drive another twelve miles
To the next junction
And another twelve miles back.
By that time it was dark.
It took us another half-hour
To find the campsite.
It's down this narrow lane.
Half-way along we met another car.
The driver just sat there,
So we had to reverse
All the way back to the main road.
By the time we got to reception,
It was closed.
It took us twenty minutes
To find the warden.
He kept complaining
That he was off duty.
Then, he couldn't find our booking-form.
'We're full up,' he said,
'Apart from the overflow field
And we're not really supposed to use that
At this time of year.'

You can tell why it's called
The overflow field.
The mud's inches thick
And it's right next to the toilet block.
I've left them putting the tent up.
I'm just phoning to let you know
We've arrived safely
And everything's fine.

It's a dog's life

Mum says
Our dog's
Having an identity crisis.

Yesterday,
He went out into the garden,
Then tried to come back in
Through the cat-flap.

He jammed his head so tight,
No matter how hard
We pushed and pulled
It wouldn't budge.

In the end,
We had to call the fire brigade.

When Dad came home
He nearly had a fit,
When he saw
What they'd done to the door.

He called the dog
All sorts of names.
But when the dog jumped up
To beg for his evening walk,
Dad still took him.

It's not fair.
If I'd smashed the door,
I wouldn't have been allowed out
For at least two weeks!

Mrs Nugent's budgie

Yesterday,
Our neighbour Mrs Nugent
Accidentally sat on her budgie.
'How did it happen?' I asked.
'Was it flattened?' said Sally.
'Like on Tom and Jerry.'
'She'd let it out
For a fly around,' said Mum.
'And she sat down on the bed
Without noticing it was there.'
'Poor thing,' said Dad.
'It didn't stand much of a chance
With her on top of it.'
'It's not dead!' said Mum.
'It lay there stunned for a while,
Then started to twitch.
So she picked it up
And popped it back in its cage.
It looked fine when I saw it,
Except that its head
Is a bit on one side.'
'Will it be all right?' I asked.
'I expect so,' said Dad.
'It sounds a tough old bird,
Like Mrs Nugent!'

The price

There's a price for the eggs you eat,
It's the hens that have to pay,
Locked in their battery cages
Day after day after day.

'It's warm and dry,' the farmer says,
'There's plenty to drink and eat.'
But the sloping wire-mesh floor
Gives them deformed feet.

There's nowhere for them to perch.
It's hard to turn around.
They cannot spread their wings
Or forage for food on the ground.

'The profit margin's higher,'
I heard the farmer say.
'It's in everybody's interest
To keep the hens this way.'

There's a price for the eggs you eat,
It's the hens that have to pay,
Locked in their battery cages
Day after day after day.

Guided tour

'We do everything we can
To ensure that the animals
Do not suffer unnecessarily,'
Said the guide.
'Our methods of experimentation
Are constantly under review.
Take these rats, for example,
Until recently,
In order to test
The regenerative capacity
Of damaged nerve tissues,
It was necessary
To sever the nerves
Leading to one of their hind legs.
Now, a refinement of our technique
Enables us to carry out the experiment
By cutting only the nerve
To a single toe.'

'May I ask a question?'
Said a woman in a green raincoat.
'Am I to understand,
From what you just said,
That you are so concerned
About the welfare of these animals
That you no longer find it necessary
To cripple them?'

The perfect animal

Scientists in California claim to have created the perfect laboratory
animal – a mouse that can be implanted with human organs.
The Independent Magazine 20 April 1991.

'We have created,'
said the scientist,
'the perfect animal.'
He pointed proudly.
Behind the glass partition
stretched row upon row
of Perspex containers
full of mice,
stacked on the shelves like shoeboxes.
'Each of those mice
has been born without an immune system,
which means . . .'
(He paused for effect.)
'They are perfect for our purposes.
We are able to implant into them
the still-living tissue
of aborted foetuses,
and . . . ' (Again, the pause for effect.)
'They do not reject it!
All kinds of experiments
that were not possible before
are now possible.'

'Are there any drawbacks?'
asked a bespectacled young man.

'It's necessary,'
replied the scientist,
'to provide a germ-free environment,
to filter the air they breathe
and to feed them irradiated food.'

'Do you mean to say,'
said a woman in a green raincoat,
'that the only drawback
with your perfect animal
is that it cannot lead
a normal life?'

Pistol practice

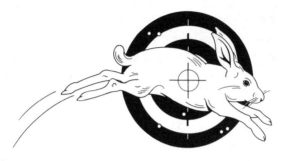

The barrel glinted in the sunlight.
I watched
As my friend pinned up
The printed target –
A small black rabbit
With a ring of white circles
Marking the spot to shoot at –
'The best place for killing it.'

The barrel glinted in the sunlight.
I watched
As my friend took aim.
The printed target
Shivered with the impact.
'Got him!' my friend said,
Pointing to the clean white hole
In the centre of the circles.

The barrel glinted in the sunlight.
I watched
As my friend casually reloaded.
The printed target blurred.

Instead I saw
A rabbit caught in mid-leap
Stagger at the bullet's punch,
Then crash to the ground,
Limp and lifeless.

'Want a go?' my friend asked.

I turned and walked indoors.

Facts about air

Scientists say
That air consists
Of about 78% nitrogen and 21% oxygen,
Plus some carbon dioxide
And small amounts
Of the rare gases – helium, argon, and neon.

These are facts, I know.
But I also know
That when I go outside
On a spring morning
The air tastes as crisp
As a fresh lettuce
And that when I sit
On the patio
On a summer evening
The cool night air
Brushes my cheeks like a feather.

Summer storm

Light travels, said Miss,
Faster than sound.
Next time there's a storm,
When you see the lightning,
Start counting slowly in seconds.
If you divide
The number of seconds by three,
It will tell you
How many kilometres you are
From the centre of the storm.

Two nights later,
I was woken
By the lashing rain,
The lightning,
And the thunder's crash.

I lay,
Huddled beneath the sheet,
As the rain poured down
And lightning lit up the bedroom,
Slowly counting the seconds,
Listening for the thunder
And calculating the distance
As the storm closed in –

Until,
With a blinding flash
And a simultaneous ear-splitting crash,
The storm passed
Directly overhead,

And I shook with fright
As the storm passed on,
Leaving the branches shuddering,
And the leaves weeping.

What is water?

A magician
Transforming deserts
With a lick of its tongue.

A conjuror
Coating ponds with ice
Or brushing your cheek with mist.

A wild animal
Plunging over cliffs,
Breaking bridges and flooding valleys.

A healer
Quenching thirst,
Rekindling the seed's flame.

A slippery customer
Slithering through your fingers,
Always on the run.

Spells

I crackle and spit. I lick and leap higher.
This is the spell of the raging fire.

I clasp and I grasp. I grip in a vice.
This is the spell of torturing ice.

I claw and I scratch. I screech and I wail.
This is the spell of the howling gale.

I clash and I crash. I rip asunder.
This is the spell of booming thunder.

I whisper. I stroke. I tickle the trees.
This is the spell of the evening breeze.

I slither. I slide. I drift and I dream.
This is the spell of the murmuring stream.

What is a shooting star?

It is a sliver of silver
that has dropped out of a hole
in the pocket of the sky.

It is a priceless coin
that slipped through a giant's fingers
while he was counting his change.

It is a magic message
flashing briefly across the night's screen
before vanishing forever.

Moons

The new moon
Is curved like a banana –
A bright C
Stamped on the sky's black page.

The old moon
Is round like a grapefruit –
A shiny button
Sewn on the sky's dark coat.

November

November is a grey road
Cloaked in mist.
A twist of wood-smoke
In the gathering gloom.
A scurrying squirrel
Hoarding acorns,
A steel-grey river
Glinting in the twilight.
A grey rope
Knotted around a threadbare tree.

Winter

Whirling snow and whistling wind
Icy patterns on window panes
Numb fingers and freezing toes
Trees stripped bare
Earth bone-hard
Roaring fires and long, dark nights.

It's spring

It's spring
And the garden is changing its clothes,
Putting away
Its dark winter suits,
Its dull scarves
And drab brown overcoats.

Now it wraps itself in green shoots,
Slips on blouses
Sleeved with pink and white blossom,
Pulls on skirts of daffodil and primrose,
Snowdrop socks and purple crocus shoes,
Then dances in the sunlight.

In the still dark

In the still dark,
High above the meadow,
The barn owl hovers,
Ear flaps erect,
Listening.

In the still dark,
Down in the meadow,
The small brown fieldmouse
Crunches the corn husk,
Unsuspecting.

In the still dark,
High above the meadow,
The barn owl swivels,
With deadly precision
Pinpointing its prey.

In the still dark,
Down towards the meadow,
The barn owl
Plunges silently,
Talons outstretched.

In the still dark,
Down in the meadow,
The barn owl
Strikes.

Arctic skua

The Arctic skua
Is a bully bird.
Like a pirate
It patrols the seashore
On the lookout
For plunder.
Spotting a tern
With a fish in its beak,
It gives chase,
Mounting a relentless pursuit,
Until the tern,
Frightened and flustered,
Drops its catch.

The skua pounces.

Having tasted success,
The robber
Returns to its vigil,
Scanning the shoreline
For its next victim.

Christmas 1992

Under a threadbare blanket, on a mattress of stone,
A teenager shivers, cold and alone.

High on a mountainside, on a carpet of snow,
A refugee waits with nowhere to go.

Under a blistering sky, on a cushion of sand,
A starving child squats and holds out her hand.

TV Wars (1991 version)

We sat in our living-rooms and watched
With a mixture of awe and pride
As the bombs poured from the sky
And Iraqi soldiers died.

We sat in our living-rooms and watched
The scenes on the mountainside,
With a mixture of horror and guilt
As Kurdish families died.

We sat in our living-rooms and watched,
Feeling powerless we sighed,
As the Serbian troops advanced
And Croatian people died.

We sat in our living-rooms and watched,
'What else can we do?' we cried,
As we silently wrote out cheques,
Passing by on the other side.

'It isn't right to fight'

You said, 'It isn't right to fight,'
But when we watched the news tonight,
You shook your fist and said
You wished the tyrant and his cronies dead.
When I asked why,
If it's not right to fight,
You gave a sigh.
You shook your head
And sadly said,
'Sometimes a cause is just
And, if there is no other way,
Perhaps, you must.'

Who's to say?

(On the fiftieth anniversary of the battle of
El Alamein, October 1992)

Great-grandmother said:
'Fifty years ago today,
your great-grandfather was killed.
They say it was the battle
that turned the tide of the war –
the first great Allied victory.
Ten thousand of our young men died.
They calculated the sacrifice was worth it.
Who's to say?
All I know is,
if there had been no war,
he might still be here
today.'

One of the many

No more waiting for the knock on the door.
No more crouching on the cellar floor.

No more listening to the TV lies.
No more disguising the look in your eyes.

No more watching what you say on the phone.
No more the feeling that you're never alone.

No more editing every word that you say.
No more curfew at the end of each day.

No more censoring what you're able to know.
No more following wherever you go.

No more being told what to think, what to do,
Except to stand here, to wait in the queue –

One of the many, not one of the few,
A free refugee.

Olympic circles

While they circled the track,
Muscles straining, lungs bursting,
In search of gold,
Elsewhere, lips cracked, stomachs knotted,
Others trudged under the same sun
In search of food,
While overhead the vultures circled.

I dream of a time

I dream of a time

When the only blades are blades of corn
When the only barrels are barrels of wine
When the only tanks are full of water
When the only chains are chains of hands

I hope for a time . . .

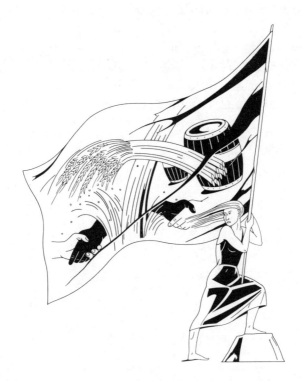

Sing a song of censorship

Sing a song of censorship, a pocketful of lies,
Four-and-twenty officers, each with eagle eyes,
Checking every column, forging every link –
Say thank you to the gentlemen who tell us what to
   think.

Beware the Smile-a-Lot

Beware the Smile-a-Lot
His welcome is not what it seems;
Behind his outstretched hand
He is cunningly hatching schemes.

Taking sides

We're canvassing opinions.
We'd simply like to know
Exactly where you stand,
How far you're prepared to go.

If it comes to the crunch,
What will you do?
Are you one of us?
Can we count on you?

We'd much appreciate it,
If you would just sign.
We knew you'd understand.
Here, on the dotted line.

Standing on the sidelines

I'm standing on the sidelines,
Practising with a ball,
Developing my skills,
Waiting for your call.

I'm standing on the platform,
Waving at each train,
Wondering if, and when or where
I'll catch a ride again.

I'm standing in the courtroom,
Accused of the crime
Of trying to scrape a living
While idly killing time.

I'm standing in the corridor.
I'm waiting in the queue.
I'd rather not be here,
But it's what I have to do.

Scene switching

Standing outside the Head's office,
I wish that I could fast forward
Through the scene
In which she's going to tell me off
And decide what punishment to give me.

Or that I could rewind the tape
To before break,
Then replay the scene
In which Tracey and I quarrelled.

Only this time, I'd play it differently.

The sporting spirit

On Sports Day, my friend Sally sat
With her back to the track,
Refusing to watch
Or fill in her programme.
'Who cares who wins?' she said,
And she read a magazine
Until Miss Evans snatched it from her,
Told her she was letting the side down
And sent her indoors
To write an essay on 'The sporting spirit.'

As I watched Sally stride off,
Head held high, towards our classroom,
I opened my programme
And wrote Sally's name in block capitals
Alongside the other winners.

Not the answer

Why is it
that when there's a fight
in the playground,
everyone gathers round
and starts taking sides,
even though most of them
don't know who started it
or what it's about?

Why is it
that when there's a fight
in the playground,
I join the others
and race to watch and cheer,
even though I know
deep down inside
fighting's not the answer?

And how was school today?

Each day they ask: And how was school today?
Behind my mask, I shrug and say OK.

Upstairs, alone, I blink away the tears
Hearing again their scornful jeers and sneers.

Hearing again them call me by those names
As they refused to let me join their games.

Feeling again them mock me with their glares
As they pushed past me rushing down the stairs.

What have I done? Why won't they let me in?
Why do they snigger? What's behind that grin?

Each day they ask: And how was school today?
Behind my mask, I shrug and say OK.

I dreamed a dolphin

Yesterday,
On the way to school,
I dreamed a dolphin
That cavorted happily all day,
Swimming and singing.

When I went through the school gates,
The nets ensnared me.
I spent the day
Wallowing in the shallows,
An ordinary fish.

Jane

I called for Jane as usual
But no one answered the door.
At registration Miss said:
'Jane's not in this class any more.'

Mum said she'd heard they'd moved away.
She did not know why or where.
I wonder what school Jane will go to now
And if she'll be happier there.

Dad

One Monday,
While we were at school,
He just packed a suitcase
And left.

Mum cried a lot.

Gran came to stay for a while.
She went on and on
About how much better it would be
Now that he'd gone.

We haven't heard from him since.

Sometimes,
I wonder where he is
And what he's doing.

I wonder if he
Ever thinks of me.

Every other Sunday

Every other Sunday,
I stand and wait
For Dad to pick me up
Down by the front gate.

If the weather's fine,
We visit the park or zoo.
When it rains, we sit in a café
Wondering what to do.

He asks me about school
And what I've done this week.
But everything's different now
And we find it hard to speak.

Every other Sunday,
Dead on half-past four
Dad drops me outside the house,
And waits till I've gone in the door.

Great-Grandad

Great-Grandad forgets
The time of the day,
Where he was going,
What he wanted to say.

Great-Grandad forgets
The day of the week.
He cannot recall
What we say when we speak.

Great-Grandad forgets
What he wants to do.
Sometimes when he sees me
He thinks that I'm you.

But Great-Grandad remembers
The relief and delight
The day the war ended
And they partied all night.

Great-Grandad remembers
How as a young man
He first met the girl
Who is now our great-gran.

Great-Grandad remembers
How things used to be
And I smile as he tells
His memories to me.

Great-Aunt Charlotte

Why don't you smile like you used to?
Why don't you think what you say?
Why do you dress in the darkness
Believing the night is the day?

What kind of world do you live in?
Is it blurred, distorted, and grey?
Where have you gone? I can't find you.
You seem to have drifted away.

Farewell visit

The day before the bulldozers moved in,
Grandpa took me across town by bus
To see the terraced house
Where he lived as a boy.

He pointed out where the standpipe was
And told me about the copper in the yard,
How he and his brothers shared a tin bath
Once a week.

He showed me where the privy stood
And the shed where they kept the coal
For the range on which his mother cooked
For a family of eight.

The house itself was empty,
Stripped bare, its windows boarded.
But in the yard
We found the remains of a mangle.

As we walked back to the bus-stop,
Grandpa peopled the street with his memories.

Beneath the bridge

Once, when Gran was a girl,
A river flowed
Between these banks
Its waters fresh and clear.

Now, the river bed
Is dried and cracked.
No water flows.
Instead,
Beneath the bridge,
A dirt-stained mattress
Leaks its stuffing
And plastic bags
Spew pools of rubbish.

Over the bridge,
Where Gran stood throwing sticks
Into the swirling current,
A stream of traffic roars,
Oblivious.

Then and Now

In the old days,
It took you a week
To travel from the south coast
To the Scottish border.

Now, a journey
That once took seven days
Takes less than seven hours.

In the old days,
Your journey took you
At a horse's pace
Over wooded hills
Of oak and ash and elm,
Between green fields
Where sheep and cattle grazed.

Today,
On concrete highways,
Carved at such a cost,
We race in frantic haste
From one vast conurbation
To the next,
Speed our only thought.

The landscape flashes past,
Disappearing.

Where is the forest?

Where is the forest?
cried the animals.
Where are the trees?

We needed the wood,
said the people.
Wood to make fires.
Wood to build houses.
We cut it down.

Where is the forest?
cried the animals.
Where are the trees?

We needed the land,
said the people.
Land for our cattle.
Land for our roads.
We cut it down.

Where is the forest?
cried the animals.
Where is our home?

Gone, whispered the wind.
Gone. Gone. Gone.

The Recycling Rap

Listen to me, children. Hear what I say.
We've got to start recycling. It's the only way
To save this planet for future generations –
The name of the game is reclamation.
You've got to start recycling. You know it makes sense.
You've got to start recycling. Stop sitting on the fence.
No more pussyfooting. No more claptrap.
Get yourself doing the recycling rap.

Come on and start recycling. Start today
By saving old newspapers, not throwing them away.
Don't just take them and dump them on the tip,
Tie them in a bundle and put them in the skip.

Get collecting, protecting the future's up to you.
Save all your old glass bottles and your jam jars too.
Take them to the bottle bank, then at the factory
The glass can be recycled, saving energy.

Don't chuck away that empty drink can.
Remember what I said. Start recycling, man.
Wash it, squash it, squeeze it flat and thin.
Take it to the Save-A-Can and post it in.

Listen to me, children. Hear what I say.
We've got to start recycling. It's the only way
To save this planet for future generations –
The name of the game is reclamation.
You've got to start recycling. You know it makes sense.
You've got to start recycling. Stop sitting on the fence.
No more pussyfooting. No more claptrap.
Get yourself doing the recycling rap.

Walls

All my life
I have walked on walls.

When I was little,
I stepped carefully,
Clutching my mother's hand tightly.

Later, I skipped happily along,
Secure in the knowledge
That if I fell
She would be there to pick me up
And console me.

As a student,
I strode purposefully
Towards my goal,
Masking my insecurity
With a show of confidence.

Next, surefooted,
I trod the walls I built,
Only gradually becoming aware
That the foundations
Were not as concrete as I thought.

Now, I walk slowly,
Tiptoeing along the battlements,
Fully conscious
How tightrope thin my path is.

Only one race

From start to finish
there is only one race.
Some glide effortlessly along smooth tracks
cushioned by prosperity.
Some stumble and fall
before even the first hurdle.
Others drop out at various intervals
as a result of poverty, sickness or war.
Most of us follow a zigzag course
we could not help but choose,
gradually running out of steam.

What is time?

A spool of film unwinding,
disappearing into the distance
like the dot on a TV screen.

The ceaseless ticking of a metronome
beating out the pulse of the future.

A computer code for unlocking
the order of events.

The graph on which
we measure out our memories
and calculate our dreams.

Superstition

Overnight,
The cracks in the pavement
Must have moved.
Today,
I could not avoid
Stepping on them.
What will tomorrow bring?